I MISS YOU ALREADY

Book design by
Michelle M. White Graphic Design
www.mmwgraphicdesign.com

I Miss You Already

Written by Cherisse Zelesky   Illustrated by Iana Zaalishvili

To My Nicole,

I can't imagine being,
without being your mom.

You are my greatest joy,
the sparkle in my eye,
my proudest accomplishment.

Thank you for all the moments you have given me;
I would redo them all, if given the chance.

My only complaint is that you grew up too fast.

Miki Maka Sue
I love you.

The first time I held you,
the first time I kissed your face;

it was the very beginning
that I felt my heart begin to race.

I miss you already.

3

Seeing the animals,
    when we went to the zoo,

I would put you in my lap
    and help you feed one or two.

I miss you already.

5

Baking cookies whenever it rained,

licking the spoon,

who could I blame?

I miss you already.

Watching your favorite movie
two or three times in a row,

acting out the scenes was always
the best part of the show.

I miss you already.

Swinging on swings
and playing at the park,

watching your excitement
was always my favorite part.

I miss you already.

11

Learning to swim
  and being part of the team,

    you were never embarrassed that
      your mom had the loudest scream.

I miss you already.

14

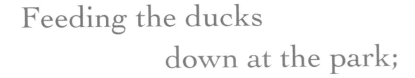

Feeding the ducks
        down at the park;

holding your bread,
        no matter how they barked.

Showing your bravery and courage too;
when they chased your little body,

        you told them what to do.

I miss you already.

At the ice capades you asked,
 "what is cotton candy?"

"Oh—its yucky stuff,
 here is your applesauce."

"Oh Mommy-you are so handy!"

I miss you already.

Leaving cookies
and milk out
for ole St. Nick,

sneaking out of
your room
was always your
favorite trick.

I miss you already.

19

Singing your heart out
   at Dad's celebration,

I'll always remember
   his total elation.

I miss you already.

21

Phone calls and dramas,
a new one every day,

heartache and tears
when friends move away.

I miss you already.

Homework, reports,
and projects always due,

at the time the days seemed endless,
but now they seem too few.

I miss you already.

Someday you will grow up
   and have a child of your own.

You will give and get more kisses
   than your heart has ever known.

You will understand
   a mother's feelings,
      so deep and so true.

I will always love you,
   my Mika Maka Sue.

26

27

I miss you already.